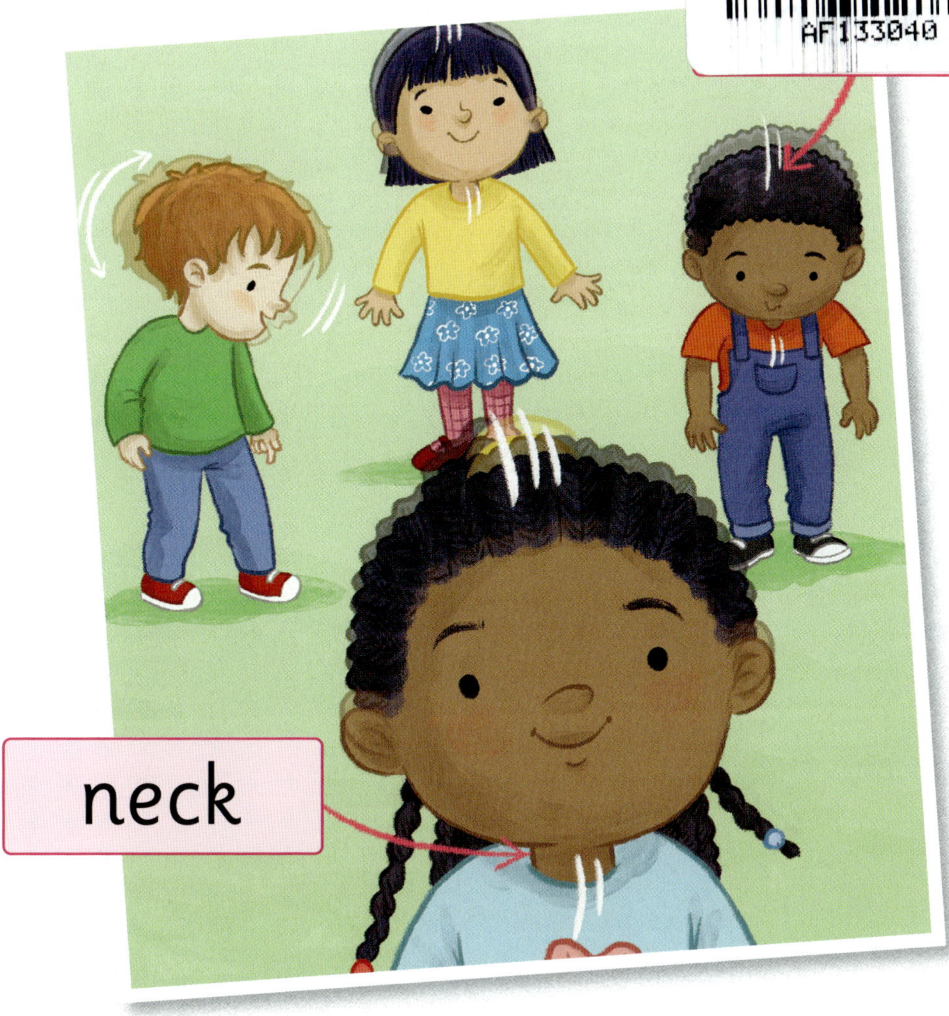

I see heads nod,

hips swing,

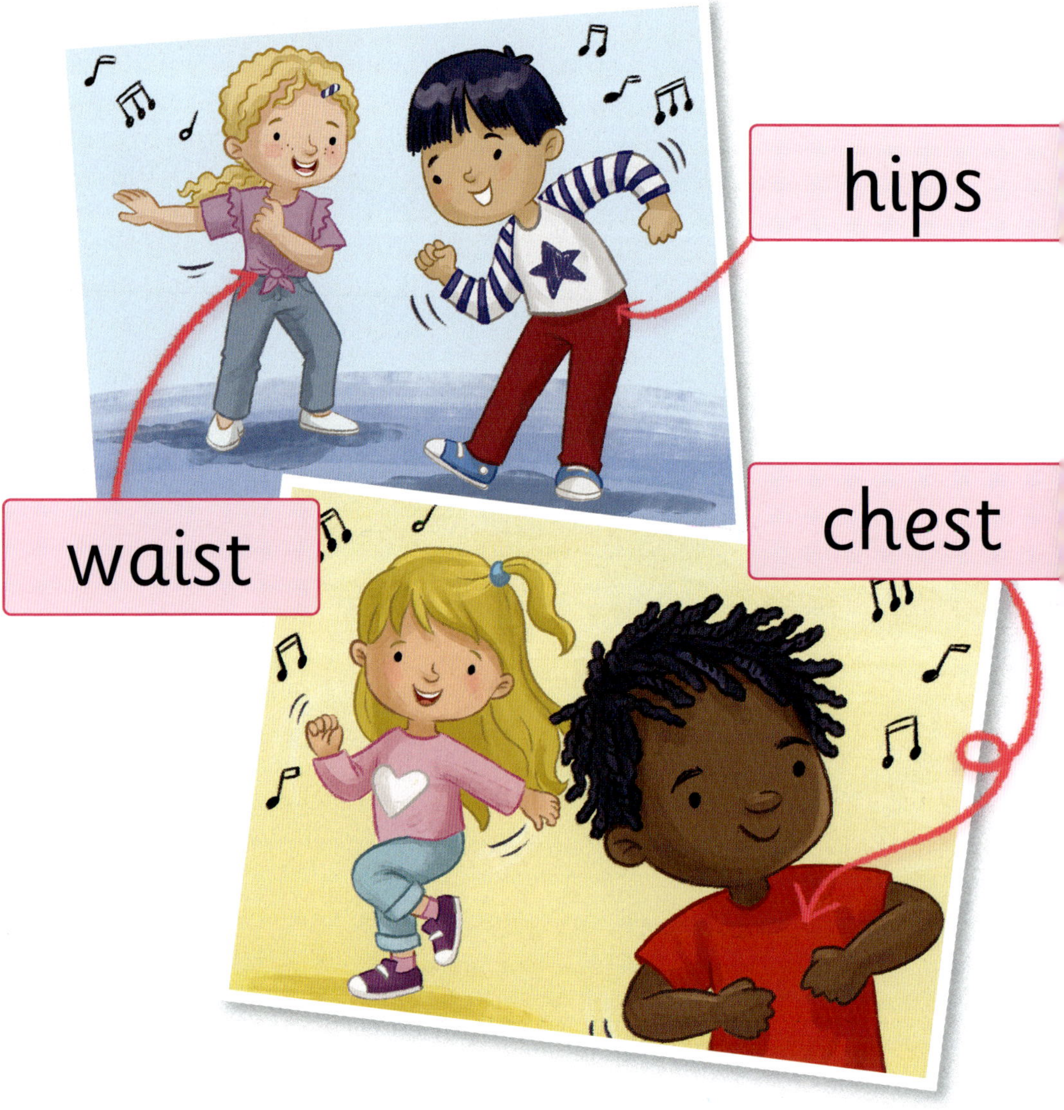
hips
waist
chest

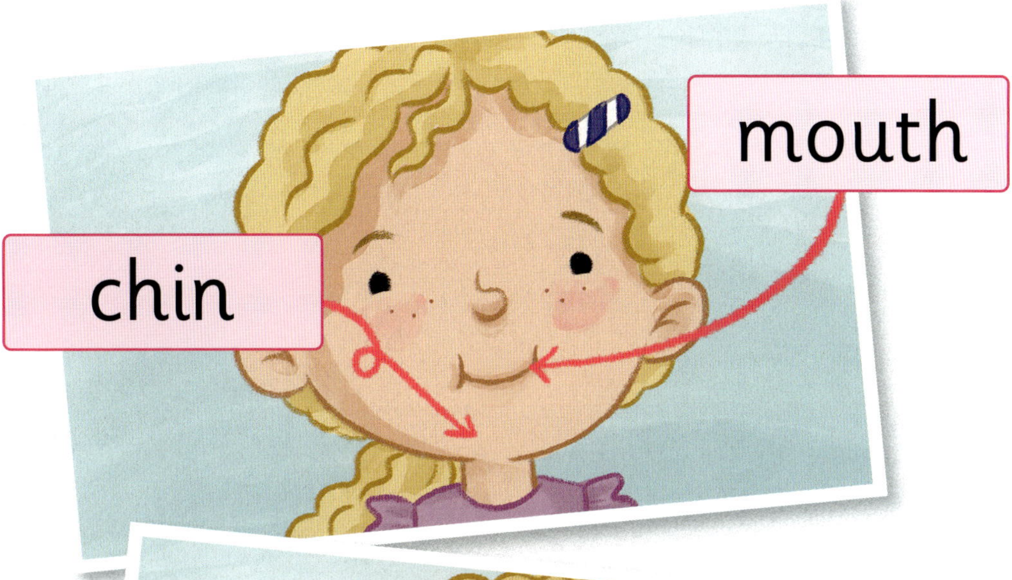
mouth
chin

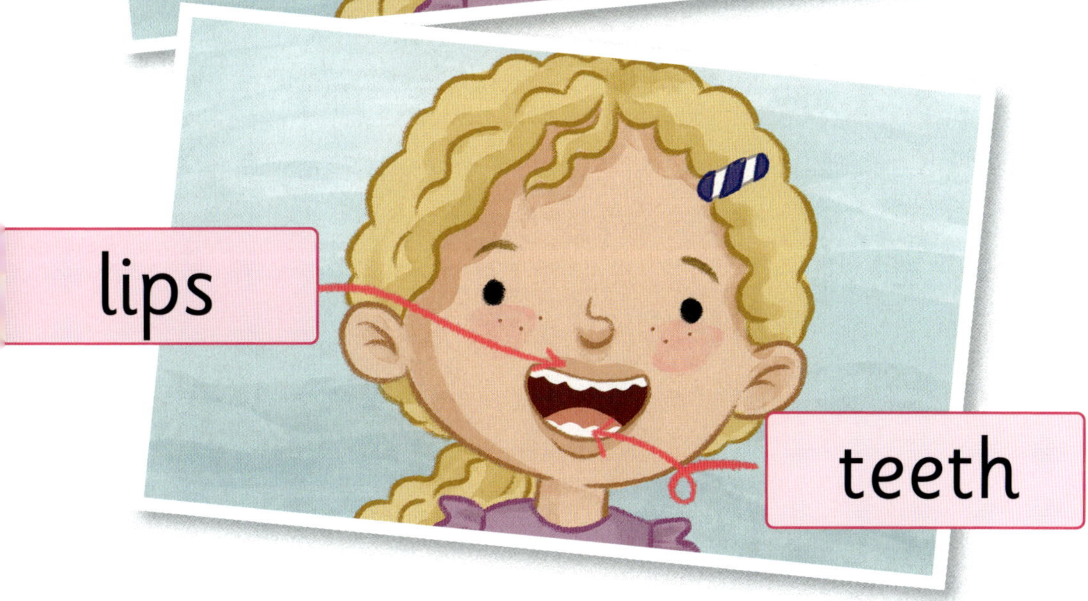
lips
teeth

lips smack,

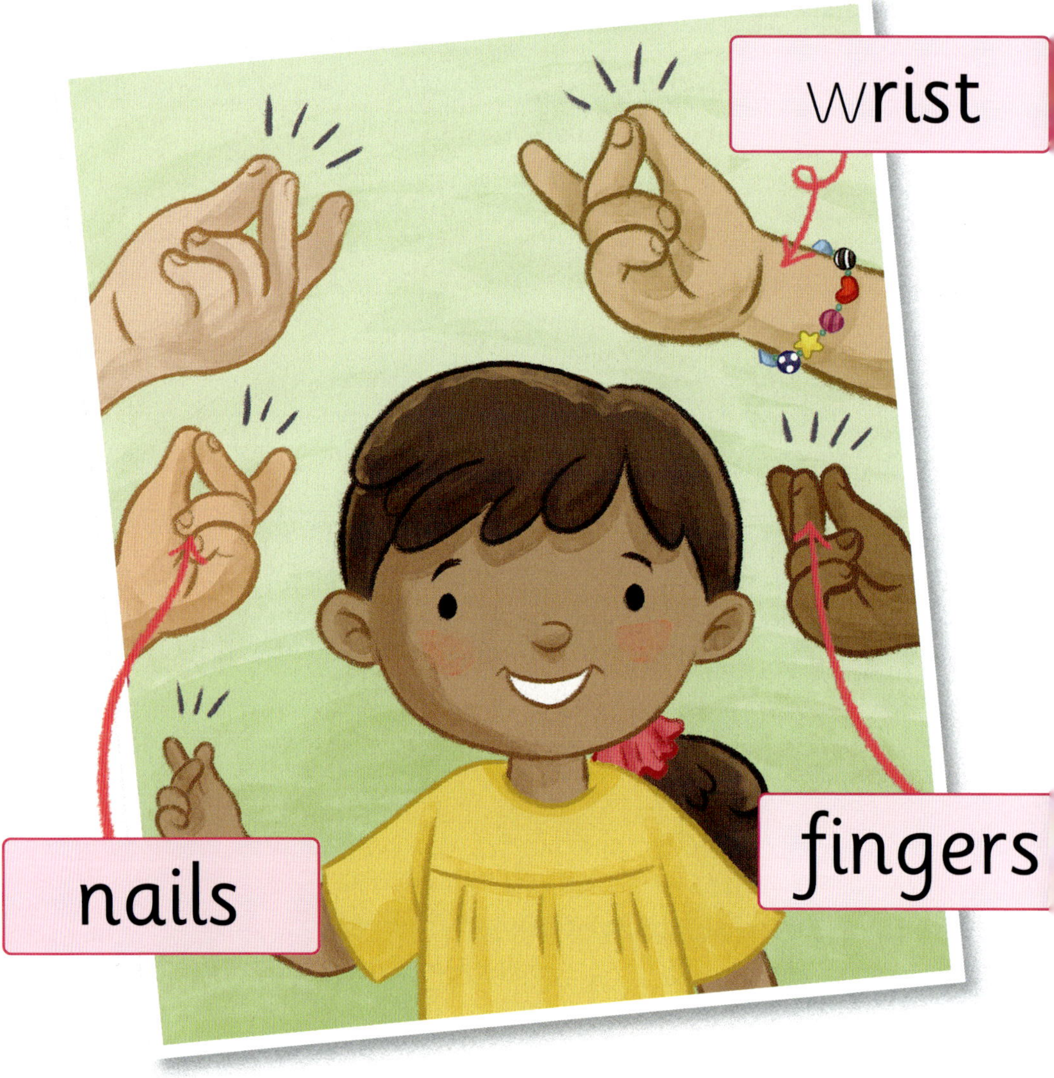

fingers click,

hands clap,

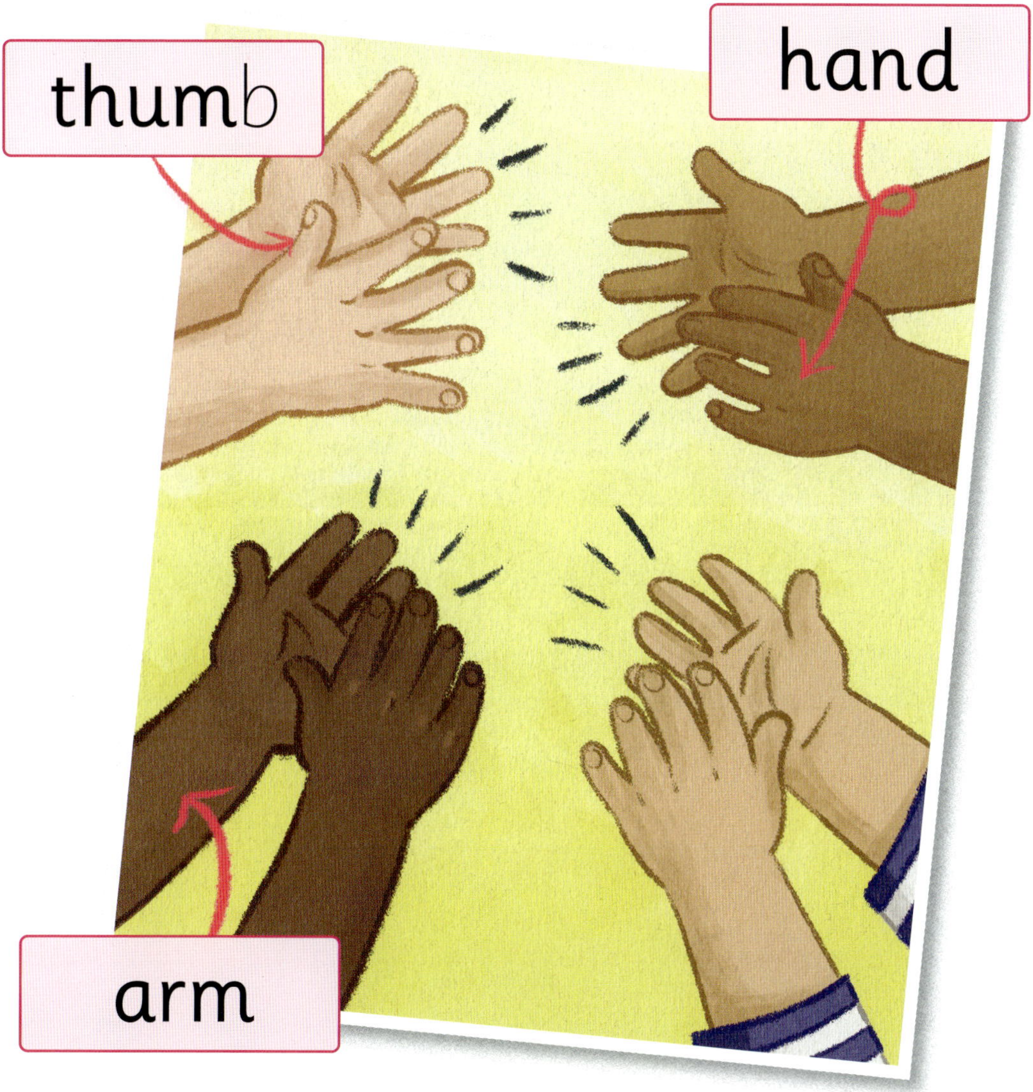
thumb
hand
arm

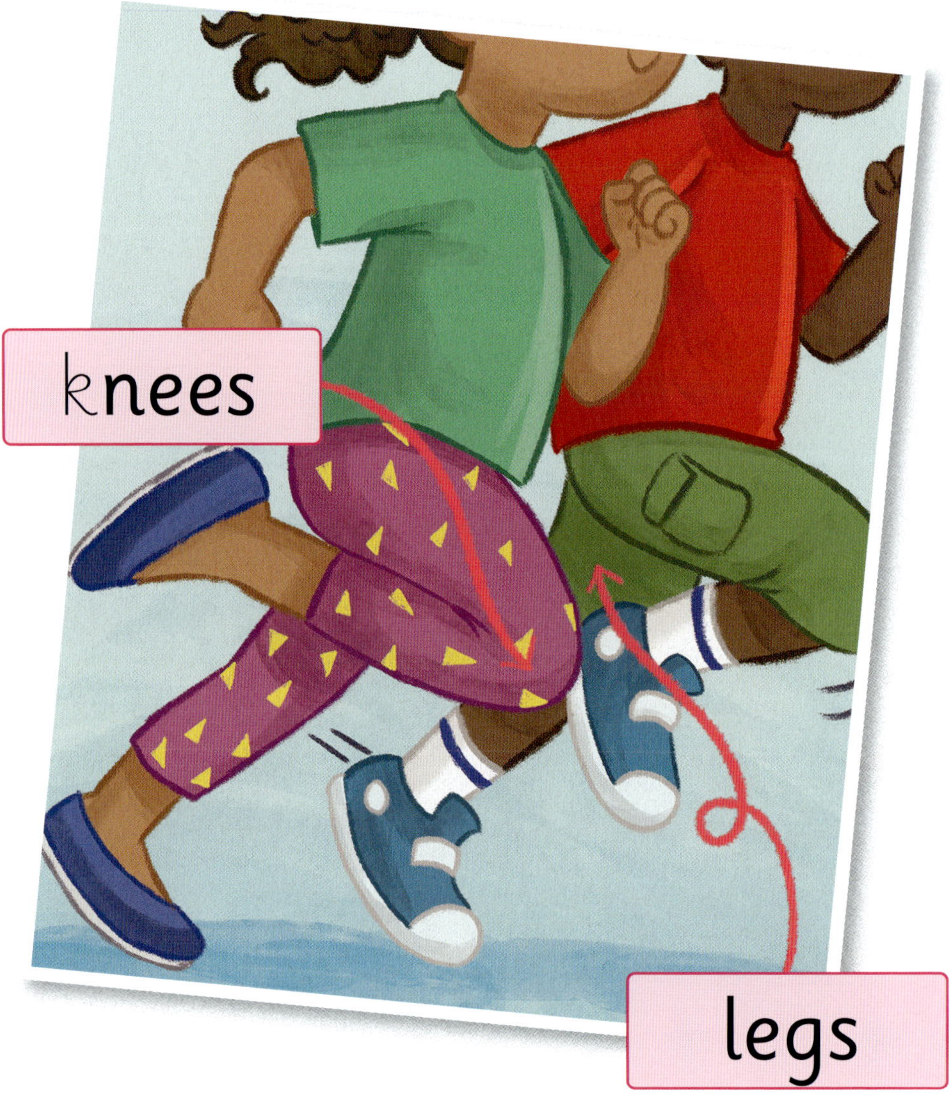

legs run and

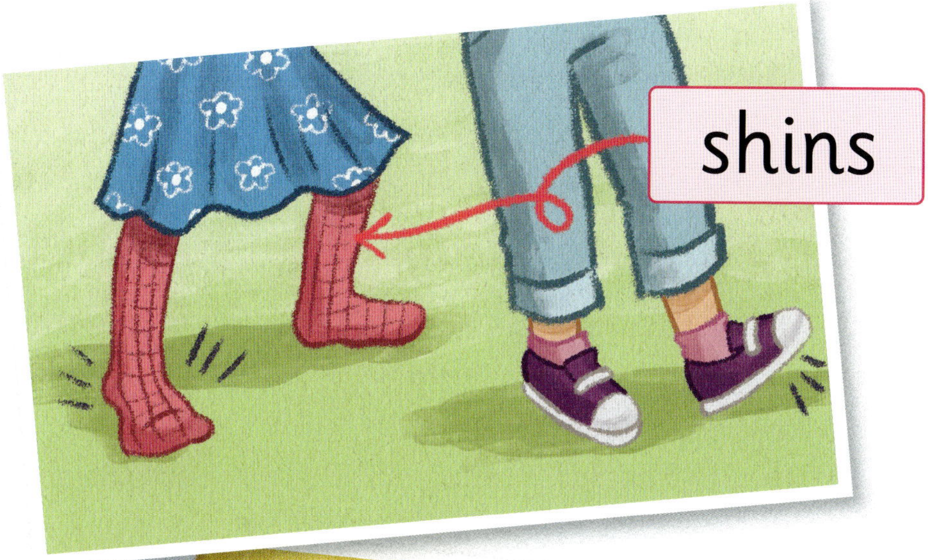

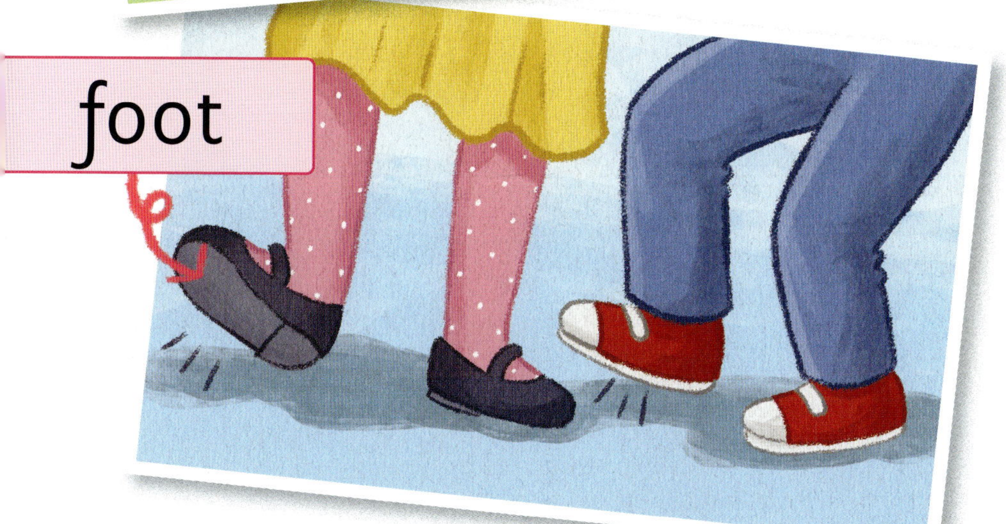

feet tap.

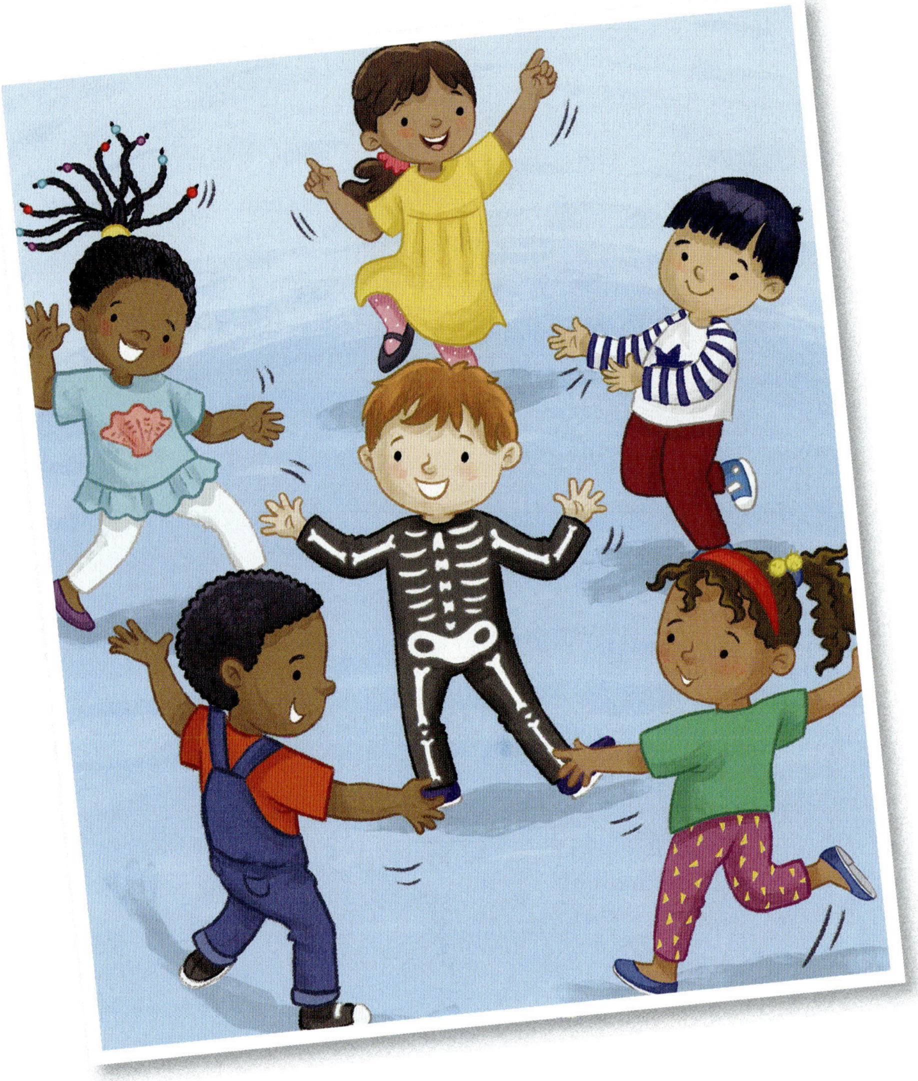

I see a skeleton!